Piano Exam Pieces

ABRSM Grade 6

Selected from the 2021 & 2022 syllabus

Name

D1581272

Date of exam

Contents

page

Editor for ABRSM: Richard Jones

Other pieces for Grade 6

Published in 2020 by ABRSM (Publishing) Ltd, a wholly owned subsidiary of ABRSM, 4 London Wall Place, London EC2Y 5AU, United Kingdom
© 2020 by The Associated Board of the Royal Schools of Music
Distributed worldwide by Oxford University Press

Unauthorised photocopying is illegal
All rights reserved. No part of this publication may be reproduced, recorded or transmitted in any form or by any means without the prior permission of the copyright owner.

Music origination by Julia Bovee
Cover by Kate Benjamin & Andy Potts, with thanks to Brighton College
Printed in England by Page Bros (Norwich) Ltd, on materials from sustainable sources.
P14656

Allegro

Fourth movement from Sonata No. 8 in C

G. B. Pescetti
(*c*.1704-66)

Giovanni Battista Pescetti was an Italian composer and keyboard player who studied with Antonio Lotti of St Mark's, Venice, and composed operas for the Venetian theatres. In the late 1730s and early 40s he worked in London as a harpsichordist and composer of operas. He then returned to Venice, composing more operas and taking up an organist's post at St Mark's.

The rounded binary form that Pescetti uses here has clear links with Classical sonata form. The exposition (bars 1–14) modulates from tonic to dominant, but when it is recapitulated at the end (bars 55–68) it is adjusted to remain in the tonic. The long, thematic and tonally adventurous section that follows the double bar (bars 15–54) is like a sonata-form development section. It modulates through several minor keys, finally cadencing in the mediant E minor at bar 54.

Dynamics are left to the player's discretion, since there are none in the source.

Source: *Sonate per gravicembalo* (London: *sine nomine*, 1739)

© 2002 by The Associated Board of the Royal Schools of Music
Adapted from *Selected Piano Examination Pieces 2003–2004*, edited by Richard Jones (ABRSM)

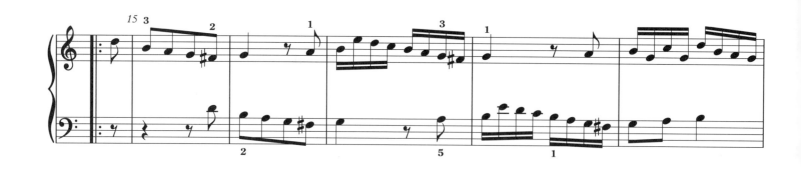

A:2

Allegro

Third movement from Sonata in E flat, K. 282

W. A. Mozart
(1756–91)

The Sonata in E flat, K. 282, is the fourth of a set of six piano sonatas that the 19-year-old Mozart composed while staying in Munich in early 1775. They are his earliest surviving piano sonatas. In 1777 he wrote to his father Leopold from Augsburg: 'Here and at Munich I have played all my six sonatas [in public] by heart several times.'

Denis Matthews (co-editor of the ABRSM edition) describes this movement as 'irresistibly lively and brilliant'. It is a sonata-form structure, in which the main theme (bars 1–8) consists of pairs of repeated notes echoed by the left hand. A dotted-rhythm idea (bars 9–15) acts as a transition to the dominant-key theme (bars 16–39), with its *piano* and *forte* phrases in alternation, each varied. The development (bars 40–61) is entirely devoted to the main theme, whose right- and left-hand parts are interchanged at bars 48–55. The movement ends with a lightly varied reprise of the exposition (bars 62–102; cf. 1–39).

The young Mozart used a short stroke or wedge sign to indicate normal staccato, an accent, or a combination of the two. Here it appears to mean just staccato.

Source: autograph MS, Biblioteka Jagiellońska, Kraków

The Spinning Top

A:3

Snurretoppen

No. 2 from *Humoreske-Bagateller*, Op. 11

Carl Nielsen
(1865–1931)

The Danish composer Carl Nielsen studied violin and composition at the Copenhagen Conservatory (1884–6). From 1889 to 1905 he was employed as a violinist in the Danish court orchestra, and later he worked as a music teacher and conductor in Copenhagen. He often travelled to other European and Scandinavian countries to direct performances of his own music.

This piece is taken from Nielsen's *Humoreske-Bagateller*, Op. 11, of 1897. Bagatelles are short pieces in a light style, and the term 'humoreske' gives an indication of their contents: they are a set of six short, lively pieces of a fanciful character, reflected in their titles: 'The Jumping Jack', 'Puppet March' etc. To illustrate the spinning top Nielsen uses the same six-note motif that Schubert had used 80 years before in his song 'Gretchen at the Spinning Wheel'.

Sources: *Humoreske-Bagateller*, Op. 11: autograph MS, dated 12.5.1897, Copenhagen, Det Kongelige Bibliotek, CNS 12a; first edition, Copenhagen & Leipzig: W. Hansen, 1897. The LH crotchets are notated as tied quavers in the sources.

B:1

Mazurka in G minor

Op. 67 No. 2

Fryderyk Chopin
(1810–49)

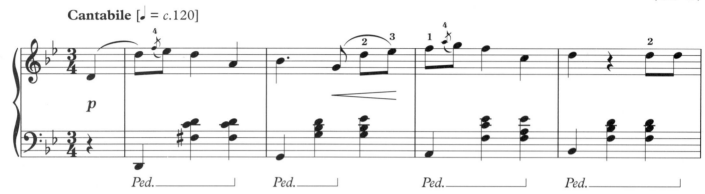

The mazurka originated as a Polish folk dance from the province of Mazovia, near Warsaw. It is in triple time with an accent on the second or third beat and was traditionally accompanied by a bagpipe drone. It became very popular as a drawing-room dance in Western Europe in the 1830s and 1840s, and the Polish composer Chopin wrote more than 50 of them. He also had a nationalistic interest in the mazurka, which is reflected in his adoption of certain melodic and rhythmic features of Polish folk music in his stylisation of the dance.

This Mazurka was composed in the last year of Chopin's life (1849) and published posthumously in 1855. Like many of his keyboard dances, it is written in ternary form (ABA). The A section cadences in the tonic, G minor, at bar 16. It is followed by a contrasting B section in the relative major, B flat, with a striking chromatic answering phrase marked **pp** *e legatissimo* (bars 21–4). A *sotto voce* solo for the right hand reintroduces the tonic key and heralds the return of section A.

The **f** in bars 14 and 54 clearly means a sudden emphasis (rather like **sf**) rather than a sustained dynamic.

Sources: *Quatre Mazurkas*, Op. 67: German first edition (Berlin: M. Schlesinger, 1855); French first edition (Paris: J. Meissonnier fils, 1855). Slurs to grace notes are editorial, except in bars 6, 17 and 19.

continued overleaf

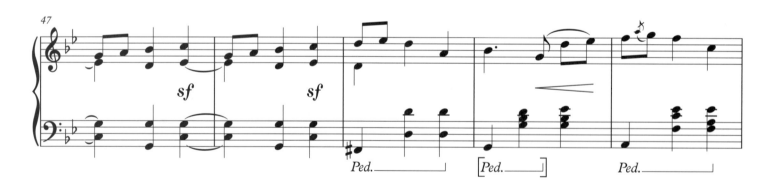

Albumleaf

Page d'album

Claude Debussy
(1862–1918)

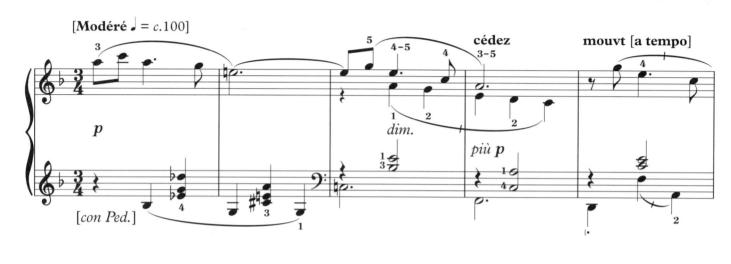

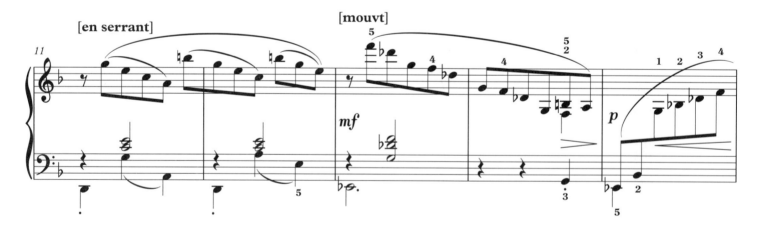

Claude Debussy, a very influential French composer of the late 19th and early 20th century, studied piano, theory and composition at the Paris Conservatoire from 1872 to 1884. As winner of the 'Prix de Rome', a highly coveted composition prize, he travelled to Rome and stayed there from 1885 to 1887. He often toured England, Russia and other European countries, performing his own music as pianist and conductor.

Debussy's mature piano music is regarded by many as the most original contribution to the repertoire since Chopin. *Page d'album* (Albumleaf) is a miniature example of his late style. It was composed in 1915 in aid of those wounded in the First World War, but not published until 1933, long after Debussy's death. The title 'page d'album' was common in the 19th century and originally used for a short piano piece written in the autograph album of a friend or patron. Later, as here, it was simply used as a fanciful title for a miniature piece of music.

Sources: autograph MS, Paris, Bibliothèque nationale, département de la musique, Ms. 14522; first edition in periodical *The Etude*, March 1933. The print is entitled *Page d'album*; the autograph has no title, but is prefaced by the words 'Pour l'oeuvre du "Vêtement du blessé"' (For the work of clothing the wounded).

First Sorrow

Erster Schmerz

from *Sechs kleine Stücke für Anfänger*

B:3

Johanna Senfter
(1879–1961)

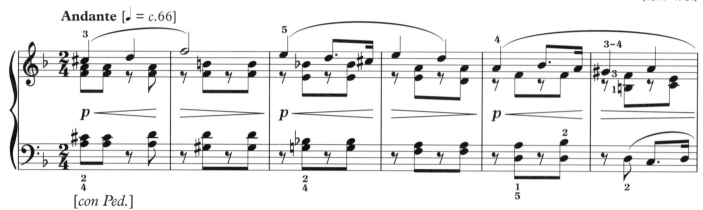

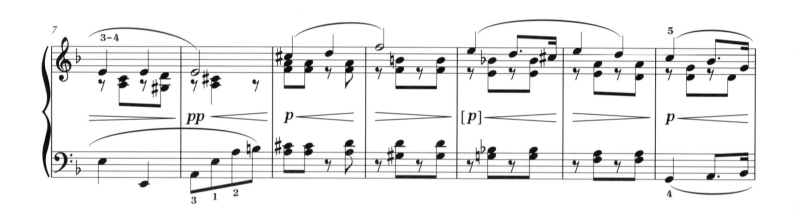

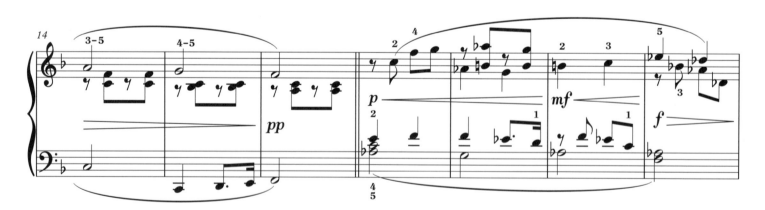

Johanna Senfter was a German composer who was born and died in Oppenheim on the Rhine. From 1895 she studied piano, violin and composition at the conservatory in Frankfurt am Main, and in 1907 became a student of Max Reger. She later returned to Oppenheim, where she was active as a composer, composition teacher and performer. She was a prolific composer (with 134 opus numbers to her credit) in a late Romantic style, and wrote in all the standard genres.

This piece, from *Six Easy Pieces for Beginners*, belongs to a type of programme music in which the title identifies the mood that the composer intends to convey. It is designed in da capo form (ABA), in which the B section (from bar 33), though in the same key of D minor, provides some degree of light relief. At the end of B (bar 46), the notes C♯ and D both echo the preceding cadence (bars 44–5) and anticipate the return of A (bar 1).

Fine

L'istesso Tempo [♩. = c.66]

D.C. al Fine

Opening Night Jazz

from *Jazz, Rags & Blues*, Book 5

Martha Mier
(born 1936)

Martha Mier is a piano teacher, composer and adjudicator in Lake City, Florida, USA. She specialises in writing educational piano music, and is widely known for her popular series *Jazz, Rags & Blues* and *Romantic Impressions*.

The Buccaneer

from *Eight Children's Pieces*, Op. 36

C:2

Malcolm Arnold
(1921–2006)

The English composer Sir Malcolm Arnold studied with Gordon Jacob at the Royal College of Music in London. In the 1940s he played the trumpet in the London Philharmonic Orchestra. After a period of further study in Italy (1948–9), he devoted himself entirely to composition.

'The Buccaneer', from Op. 36 written in 1952, gives a vivid musical portrait of a swashbuckling pirate. After a *fortissimo* prologue (bars 1–6), an accompaniment begins (bars 7–8) and we can imagine the pirate singing boldly of his exploits (bars 9–12). This tune returns twice (at bars 18 and 29), alternating with passages full of dissonant repeated chords that seem to evoke the ferocity of the pirate's life (starting at bars 13, 22 and 33). Finally, the opening bars return as an epilogue (from bar 38).

Lavender Field

Karen Tanaka
(born 1961)

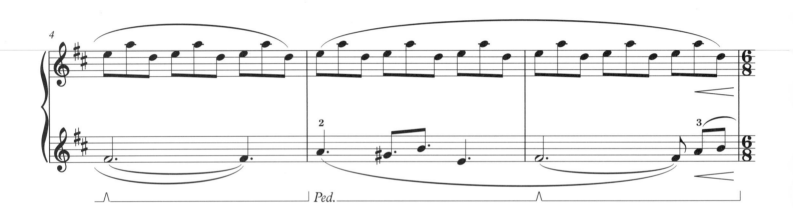

The Japanese composer Karen Tanaka studied composition and piano at the Toho Gakuen School of Music in Tokyo, Japan. In 1986 she moved to Paris, France, where she worked at IRCAM, the research institute run by Pierre Boulez. Later (1990–91) she studied with Luciano Berio in Florence, Italy. She has taught in several American universities, and now lives in Los Angeles, teaching composition at the California Institute of the Arts.

Tanaka's love of nature and concern for the environment are reflected in many of her compositions. 'Lavender Field' was written in Paris on 5 February 2000 for inclusion in *Spectrum 3, an international collection of 25 pieces for solo piano*, published by ABRSM. The composer has written: 'Imagine weaving colour and scent with sounds. The harmonic series on E♭ appears and disappears into space at the end.'